REZIUM STUDIOS PRESENTS. . .

Super Indian

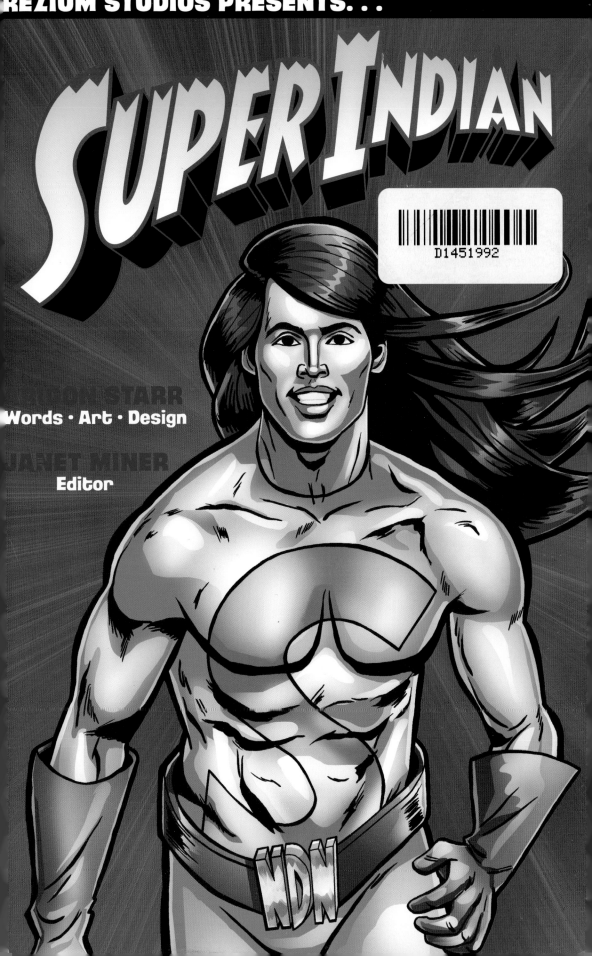

ARIGON STARR

Words · Art · Design

JANET MINER

Editor

D1451992

SUPER INDIAN: VOLUME TWO
Published by Wacky Productions Unlimited.
Cover and compilation Copyright ©2015
Wacky Productions Unlimited.
All Rights Reserved.

Super Indian Online Webcomic
Updated EVERY Monday
www.superindiancomics.com

All characters, their distinctive likenesses and related element
featured in this publication are trademarks of Arigon Star
Rezium Studios and Wacky Productions Unlimited. The stories
characters and incidents featured in this publication are entire
fictional. Wacky Productions Unlimited does not read or accep
unsolicited submissions of ideas, stories or artwork

Wacky Productions Unlimite
PO Box 4615
West Hollywood, CA 90046-015
Printed in Korea. First Printing
ISBN: 978-0-9859535-2-

Super special thanks to Dr. Susan Bernardin, Clementine Bordeaux
Lee Francis IV, Nasbah Hill, Shayai Lucero
and my Mom, Ruth Wahpecome
Dedicated to my mentors who've walked on
Robert J. Conley, Cecelia Okemah Frye
Charlie Hill and Bob Hicks

To my friends and family, thanks for putting up with
my radio silence and providing inspiration and laughs
to make this work that much easier

-- Arigon Starr

HEROES

Hubert Logan
A janitor at the Leaning Oak Bingo Hall....and Super Indian's secret identity.

Super Indian
The Reservation Hero ate tainted commodity cheese and gained super powers.

Diogi
The Rez Dog with super smarts.

Grandma Logan
Hubert's Grandma and Tribal medicine woman.

General Bear
Hubert's best friend.

Mega Bear
The on-duty identity of Super Indian's trusty sidekick.

Phoebe Francis
A plucky eco-tour guide and voracious reader.

Laguna Woman
Phoebe's superhero alter-ego, also known as Ka'Waika Woman.

VILLAINS

Blud Kwan'Tum
The vampire created and cursed to become a full-blood Indian or die.

Mr. Pokemonemptewa
Blud's evil Hopi henchman.

The Bee-Geen
Mischievious medicine man, evil shaman...or???

Greetings from Los Angeles!

It's an amazing time to be a comic book artist. We're receiving all sorts of attention these days, some of it good (cartoonist/graphic novelist Alison Bechdel receives a "Genius Grant" from the MacArthur Foundation), some very, very bad (the Charlie Hebdo killings).

The best part about it – I think some folks might be changing their minds about how they perceive Native American Indians. "Super Indian" and other Native comic/graphic novel projects are slowly making their way into the mass consciousness...one reader at a time!

After the publication of "Super Indian Volume One," I was thrilled to be invited to numerous comic book conventions (or 'cons' as they're better known) to talk about my work. Sitting at a convention booth after the short, fun panels was a mixed bag. Most folks who stopped by were awesome. A great number of teachers and librarians engaged me and said a book about contemporary Native Americans was a breath of fresh air. Other folks would ask me to vet their own Native American projects ("She's a shaman and shapeshifter solving mysteries!" Or – "It's a story based on the Apache. No, I'm not Apache or know anyone Apache, but I'm sure you do and can make sure my book is historically and culturally accurate!") or to talk genealogy. As you probably know, there are many Cherokee princess great-grandmothers running wild in people's histories! Only Native folks laughed out loud at my story pitch, "He ate tainted commodity cheese and gained super powers."

Folks like Debbie Reese from the American Indians in Children's Literature championed "Super Indian" from their websites. Blogger Lisa Charleyboy and publisher Mary Beth Leatherdale/Annick Press added a feature in their excellent "Dreaming In Indian" book. Even academics like Professor Susan Bernardin at SUNY College in Oneonta, New York are studying "Super Indian" and writing scholarly articles about sweet Hubert Logan, the Rezium-tainted cheese-eater! What a world!

I hope this edition of "Super Indian" stories makes you laugh, think and want to look up "Fish Camp" online. If you're Native, I know you'll appreciate the "Twilight" and "blood quantum" humor – and to those not in our community – howdy, welcome! Grab a chair, join us in the "Super Indian" Universe and prepare to laugh. It's okay to laugh at these Indians. You have my permission.

Live Long and Prosper!

Arigon Starr
Rezium Studios, February 2015

WILL ROGERS

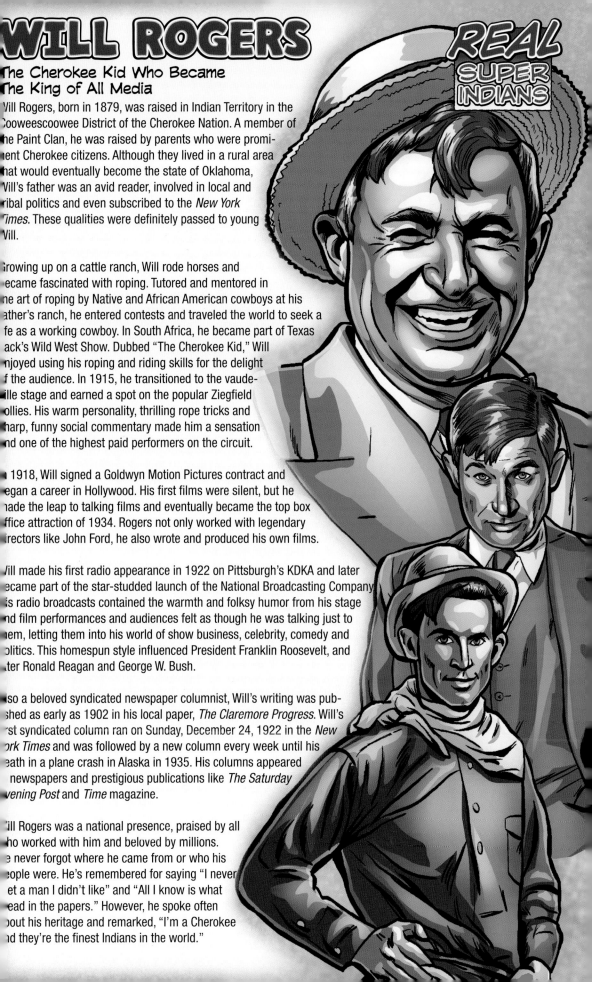

The Cherokee Kid Who Became The King of All Media

Will Rogers, born in 1879, was raised in Indian Territory in the Cooweescoowee District of the Cherokee Nation. A member of the Paint Clan, he was raised by parents who were prominent Cherokee citizens. Although they lived in a rural area that would eventually become the state of Oklahoma, Will's father was an avid reader, involved in local and tribal politics and even subscribed to the *New York Times*. These qualities were definitely passed to young Will.

Growing up on a cattle ranch, Will rode horses and became fascinated with roping. Tutored and mentored in the art of roping by Native and African American cowboys at his father's ranch, he entered contests and traveled the world to seek a life as a working cowboy. In South Africa, he became part of Texas Jack's Wild West Show. Dubbed "The Cherokee Kid," Will enjoyed using his roping and riding skills for the delight of the audience. In 1915, he transitioned to the vaudeville stage and earned a spot on the popular Ziegfield Follies. His warm personality, thrilling rope tricks and sharp, funny social commentary made him a sensation and one of the highest paid performers on the circuit.

In 1918, Will signed a Goldwyn Motion Pictures contract and began a career in Hollywood. His first films were silent, but he made the leap to talking films and eventually became the top box office attraction of 1934. Rogers not only worked with legendary directors like John Ford, he also wrote and produced his own films.

Will made his first radio appearance in 1922 on Pittsburgh's KDKA and later became part of the star-studded launch of the National Broadcasting Company. His radio broadcasts contained the warmth and folksy humor from his stage and film performances and audiences felt as though he was talking just to them, letting them into his world of show business, celebrity, comedy and politics. This homespun style influenced President Franklin Roosevelt, and later Ronald Reagan and George W. Bush.

Also a beloved syndicated newspaper columnist, Will's writing was published as early as 1902 in his local paper, *The Claremore Progress*. Will's first syndicated column ran on Sunday, December 24, 1922 in the *New York Times* and was followed by a new column every week until his death in a plane crash in Alaska in 1935. His columns appeared in newspapers and prestigious publications like *The Saturday Evening Post* and *Time* magazine.

Will Rogers was a national presence, praised by all who worked with him and beloved by millions. He never forgot where he came from or who his people were. He's remembered for saying "I never met a man I didn't like" and "All I know is what I read in the papers." However, he spoke often about his heritage and remarked, "I'm a Cherokee and they're the finest Indians in the world."

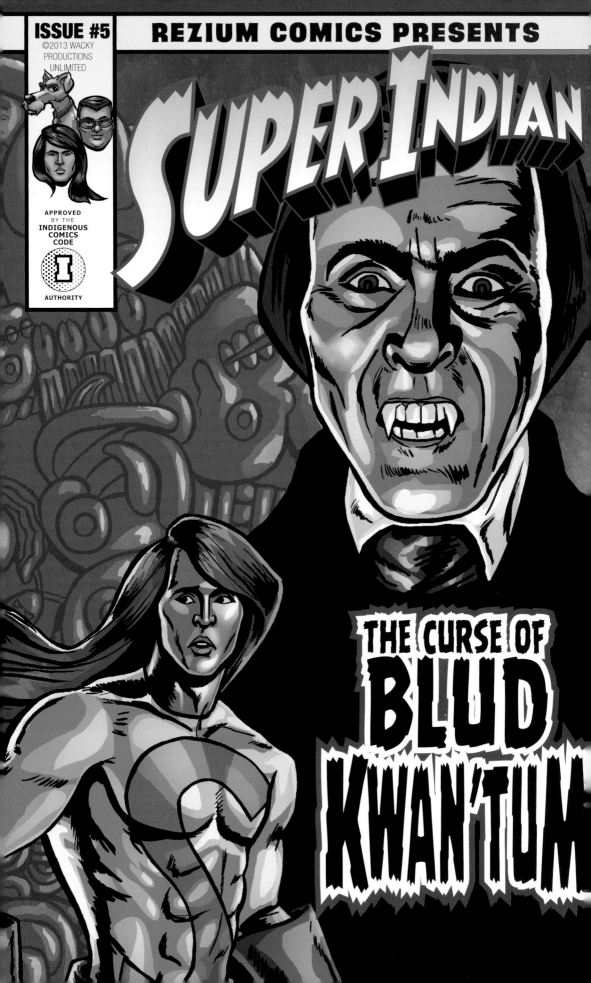

AMERICA GATHERING

what happens at I-GAG...

REAL INDIAN GUIDES. EXPLOR THE OUTDOO

I HATE "I-GAG."

I MEAN...THE "INDIAN GAMING OF AMERICA GATHERING."

THIS IS THE THIRD YEAR MY BOSS HAS SENT ME HERE.

ALONE.

OUR COMPANY SPECIALIZES IN ONE-OF-A-KIND CORPORATE GETAWAYS. OUR EXTREME VACATIONS ENCOURAGE TEAM BUILDING... "SURVIVOR" STYLE.

OUTDOOR ADVENTURE VACATIONS ARE A HARD SELL TO NATIVE PEOPLE. WHY IS THAT?

WHILE MY BOSS TAKES A GROUP OF INDUSTRY OVERACHIEVERS THROUGH SOME AWESOME MAYAN RUINS IN THE YUCATAN... I'M STUCK IN OKLAHOMA CITY.

ARIGON STARR
WRITER • PENCILS
INK • COLOR
LETTER

JANET MINER
EDITOR

IT'S DAY THREE OF THAT LAUGH.

THE BARK OF LENA MARIE. SHE MAKES ME WISH I HAD SERIOUS HEARING LOSS.

HOLY *"WRATH OF KHAN!"* LOOK AT THAT GUY!

IS HE FOR *REAL?*

WHOA!

WHO IS *THAT?*

WOULDN'T YOU KNOW IT?

HE'S GOING OVER TO TALK TO THAT AWFUL *BRAYING DONKEY WOMAN.*

HE PARTED THE CROWD WITHOUT A WORD. THIS IS GONNA BE GOOD!

GOOD AFTERNOON, MISS. MAY I INQUIRE ABOUT THE NATURE OF THE LEANING OAK RESERVATION?

I'M LENA MARIE AND THE **BOSS** OF THE TRIBE'S BINGO HALL... AND THEIR *TOURISM WRANGLER.*

HOW CAN I HELP YOU, MISTER...?

MY NAME IS NOT IMPORTANT. YOUR PEOPLE... THEY ARE *PRECIOUS.* MAY WE TALK PRIVATELY?

MISS LENA, HELP ME RESCUE NATIVE CULTURE WITH THE GUIDANCE OF YOUR *FULL-BLOOD* TRIBAL MEMBERS.

WE GOT PLENTY OF THOSE IN LEANING OAK. THEY'RE MY *BEST CUSTOMERS* ON HALF-PRICE BINGO PACK NIGHT.

ON THESE "HALF-PRICE NIGHTS," MIGHT I HAVE THE PLEASURE OF INTERVIEWING THESE ELDERS...

...FOR A FILM PROJECT?

WHEN *MR. K* ASKS YOU A QUESTION...

YOU *ANSWER!*

YOUR FIRST INSULT IS *FREE.*

I'M PART COMANCHE... AND WE *DON'T PLAY!*

OH, BROTHER. FROM ONE OPERATOR TO ANOTHER. I'M GONNA FINISH READING MY BOOK.

ANYTHING THAT HAPPENS IN THE PAGES OF *"NEVER AT DUSK"* IS FAR SUPERIOR TO THIS BLEAK LANDSCAPE.

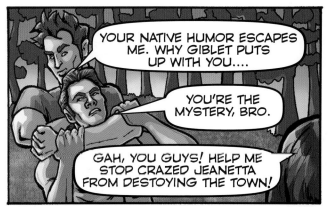

YOUR NATIVE HUMOR ESCAPES ME. WHY GIBLET PUTS UP WITH YOU....

YOU'RE THE MYSTERY, BRO.

GAH, YOU GUYS! HELP ME STOP CRAZED JEANETTA FROM DESTOYING THE TOWN!

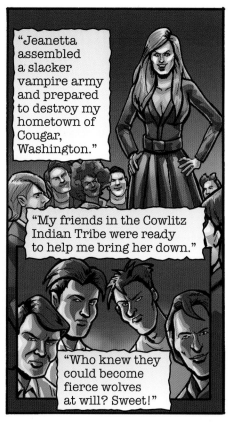

"Jeanetta assembled a slacker vampire army and prepared to destroy my hometown of Cougar, Washington."

"My friends in the Cowlitz Indian Tribe were ready to help me bring her down."

"Who knew they could become fierce wolves at will? Sweet!"

"I never meant to beat her to 'bingo.' I'm just lucky."

"How was I to know I'd ruined her one hundred card game?"

"She used vampire skills to win at Blackout."

WHERE IS SHE? I'LL *KILL* HER?

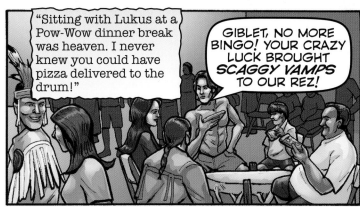

"Sitting with Lukus at a Pow-Wow dinner break was heaven. I never knew you could have pizza delivered to the drum!"

GIBLET, NO MORE BINGO! YOUR CRAZY LUCK BROUGHT *SCAGGY VAMPS* TO OUR REZ!

AN HOMAGE TO KEITH RICHARDS?

MISS! OH, MISS! *EXCUSE ME!*

"Clive and his vampire family took the threat seriously. Their fashion sense...even more so."

GIBLET... THAT'S ONE SCARF TOO MANY.

EGADS! THERE'S A FISHING LURE...

...IN... HER.. HAIR!

MISS, WILL YOU WATCH LENA MARIE'S BOOTH WHILE MY EMPLOYER AND I WHISK HER AWAY FOR A FINE DINING EXPERIENCE?

SURE, MISTER. WHATEVER.

FASHION FAUX PAS OR NOT... CLIVE WILL *NEVER* LEAVE GIBLET. BRUTAL POW-WOW REBUFF! LUKUS BETTER GET OVER IT!

AAAH...ANOTHER POSSESSED BY THE DARK POWER OF *"NEVER AT DUSK."* VAMPIRES DO HAVE ALL THE FUN.

MEANWHILE ON THE LEANING OAK RESERVATION, GENERAL BEAR BURNS THE MIDNIGHT OIL TRYING TO FINISH READING BOOK ONE OF THE "NEVER AT DUSK" SAGA.

GAH, LUKUS! GIBLET TOTALLY WANTS YOU, BUT SHE WON'T BREAK AWAY FROM CLIVE. THAT'S MY LIFE STORY. TOO MANY CLIVES TAKING THE BABES!

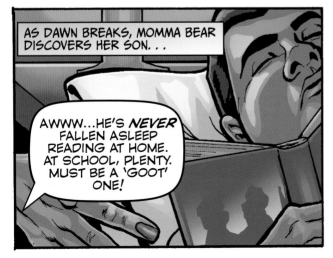

AS DAWN BREAKS, MOMMA BEAR DISCOVERS HER SON. . .

AWWW...HE'S *NEVER* FALLEN ASLEEP READING AT HOME. AT SCHOOL, PLENTY. MUST BE A 'GOOT' ONE!

MOMMA, DO WE STILL HAVE A *LIBRARY CARD*? I WANNA READ THE NEXT BOOK!

THE NEXT DAY AT THE I-GAG TRADE SHOW, LENA MARIE ROBOTICALLY HANDS OUT FLYERS. . .

VISIT LEANING OAK.

VISIT LEANING OAK *NOW.*

YOU *KNOW* YOU *WANT* TO.

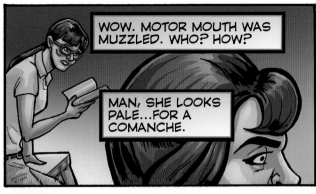

WOW. MOTOR MOUTH WAS MUZZLED. WHO? HOW?

MAN, SHE LOOKS PALE...FOR A COMANCHE.

MISS, THANK YOU FOR WATCHING LADY LENA'S BOOTH YESTERDAY. OUR DINNER WAS CHARMING AND INFORMATIVE.

MR. K, THIS YOUNG WOMAN IS READING *"NEVER AT DUSK."*

AAH...WILLIE WEINER'S MASTERWORK. MISS WEINER AND I ARE CLOSE ACQUAINTANCES.

YOU *KNOW HER?* SHE'S MEGA-FAMOUS!

WHY, YUH...I AM..UH... *PHOEBE FRANCIS.* FROM NEW MEXICO. LAGUNA PUEBLO. BUT I GREW UP HERE. IN OKLAHOMA CITY... BUT I LIVE IN SAN FRANCISCO AND....

...YOU WORK FOR BRODY BORDEAUX, A LAKOTA TOUR GUIDE. WE TRAVELED THE MOUNTAINS OF PUEBLA AND HE LED OUR B-I-A GROUP THROUGH AN *ANCIENT AZTEC RUIN.* I SHALL *NEVER* FORGET IT.

I SHARED TRIBAL LEGENDS WITH HER. INVALUABLE KNOWLEDGE GAINED FROM *FULL-BLOOD* ELDERS. WHERE ARE *YOU* FROM, MISS? YOU LOOK FAMILIAR.

ME? OH... I'M NOBODY SPECIAL.

AT THE BINGO HALL...

SO THEN...SHE PINES AFTER THE VAMPIRE GUY WHEN HE RUNS AWAY TO EUROPE. I LAUGHED. I CRIED. I COULD TOTALLY RELATE TO GIBLET. SHE'S MY GIRL.

GIBLET? WHAT KIND OF NAME IS THAT?

HUBERT, YOU MORON! "NEVER AT DUSK" HAS A NATIVE HEART. ALL THE INDUNS ARE *COOL* IN THIS BOOK. THEY'RE FULL-ON *WEREWOLVES!*

IF THEY *EVER* MAKE A *MOVIE* OUT OF THIS BOOK...

I'M GOING TO *HOLLYWOOD!*

GENERAL BEAR... THERE *IS* A "NEVER AT DUSK" MOVIE! REMEMBER THE *CONTROVERSY?* THEY WOULDN'T CAST *CAL VAN ERIK* AS THE LEAD WEREWOLF BECAUSE THE MOVIE PEOPLE THOUGHT HE WAS TOO OLD FOR THE PART.

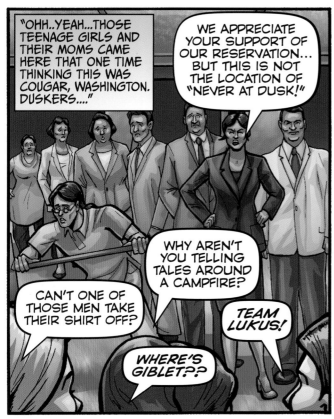

"OHH..YEAH...THOSE TEENAGE GIRLS AND THEIR MOMS CAME HERE THAT ONE TIME THINKING THIS WAS COUGAR, WASHINGTON. DUSKERS...."

WE APPRECIATE YOUR SUPPORT OF OUR RESERVATION... BUT THIS IS NOT THE LOCATION OF "NEVER AT DUSK!"

WHY AREN'T YOU TELLING TALES AROUND A CAMPFIRE?

CAN'T ONE OF THOSE MEN TAKE THEIR SHIRT OFF?

TEAM LUKUS!

WHERE'S GIBLET??

AS TOURISM LIAISON FOR THE LEANING OAK TRIBE, IT WOULD BE WRONG FOR ME TO SLAP SOME OF YOU UPSIDE YOUR HEAD... HOWEVER....

IF YOU BEHAVE, THERE'S A GUIDED TOUR OF THE REZ IN IT FOR ALL OF YOU.

I'LL GIVE THEM A TOUR THEY'LL *NEVER* FORGET, CARRIE!

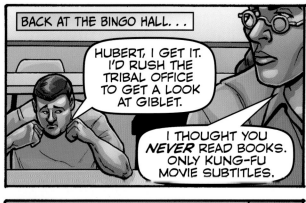

BACK AT THE BINGO HALL...

HUBERT, I GET IT. I'D RUSH THE TRIBAL OFFICE TO GET A LOOK AT GIBLET.

I THOUGHT YOU *NEVER* READ BOOKS. ONLY KUNG-FU MOVIE SUBTITLES.

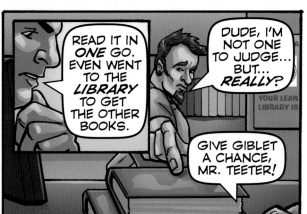

READ IT IN *ONE* GO. EVEN WENT TO THE *LIBRARY* TO GET THE OTHER BOOKS.

DUDE, I'M NOT ONE TO JUDGE... BUT... *REALLY?*

GIVE GIBLET A CHANCE, MR. TEETER!

SEE, THEY'RE *ALL INDUNS* TO ME...

CLIVE, THE STUCK-UP CROW GUY....

GIBLET, THE BEAUTIFUL NEZ PERCE GIRL...

LUKUS... HE'S SO LEANING OAK!

WELL...IN THE MOVIE GIBLET AND CLIVE ARE WHITE PEOPLE. THE GUY WHO PLAYED LUKUS...

...MADE A *BIG STAR* OF A *NATIVE AMERICAN ACTOR,* RIGHT?

YOU NEED TO SEE THE *TRUTH.* MEET ME IN THE LUNCH ROOM IN FIVE MINUTES.

CLIVE! THE *SUNLIGHT!* SPARKLE, CLIVE! *SPARKLE!*

NO? NO... NO!!!

THAT'S WHAT WE SAY WHEN LENA MARIE HAS THIS MOVIE ON IN HER OFFICE.

THE I-GAG TRADESHOW CONTINUES...

SO, THAT'S WHY "REAL INDIAN GUIDES" PROVIDE THE MOST VALUE FOR YOUR TOURIST AND TEAMBUILDING DOLLAR.

SERIOUSLY, YOU GET *MUCH MORE* THAN YOU BARGAINED FOR WITH OUR SERVICE!

GUYS... WE WON'T TAKE CLIENTS TO *SACRED SITES* OR CONDUCT *SWEAT LODGES!*

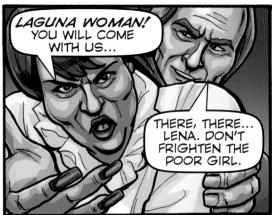

LAGUNA WOMAN! YOU WILL COME WITH US...

THERE, THERE... LENA. DON'T FRIGHTEN THE POOR GIRL.

MISS FRANCIS, I WOULD BE HONORED IF YOU WOULD JOIN US FOR DINNER.

WOW!...UM...SURE. WHERE SHOULD I MEET YOU, MISTER... MISTER..WHAT IS YOUR NAME?

I AM...BLUD... *BLUD KWAN'TUM.*

MR. POKEMONEMPTEWA, PLEASE ARRANGE TO HAVE HER BOOTH PACKED UP AND SHIPPED TO THE LEANING OAK RESERVATION.

RIGHT AWAY, MR. K.

BUT, I'M NOT GOING THERE...

YES, YOU *ARE,* LAGUNA WOMAN!

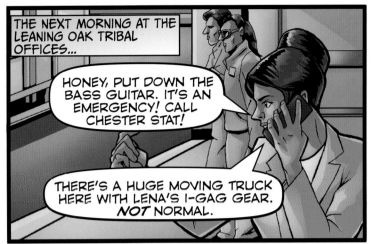

THE NEXT MORNING AT THE LEANING OAK TRIBAL OFFICES...

HONEY, PUT DOWN THE BASS GUITAR. IT'S AN EMERGENCY! CALL CHESTER STAT!

THERE'S A HUGE MOVING TRUCK HERE WITH LENA'S I-GAG GEAR. *NOT* NORMAL.

ALL RIGHT, DEAR. WE'RE ALMOST FINISHED LEARNING THAT REDBONE SONG. I'LL BUZZ CHESTER NOW!

AT THE TRIBAL RADIO STATION...

NDN TACO SALE SAT 2

CONCERT

LINE TWO, YOU'RE ON "THE TRADER!"

UNCLE CHESTER! MICK LOGAN CALLING FROM BAND PRACTICE. HOT NEWS! *BIG MOVING TRUCK* AT THE TRIBAL OFFICE.

WHOA! THE BOARD HAS LIT UP LIKE FIRECRACKERS!

MAYBE CHIEF YELLOWSHIRT IS *FINALLY* STEPPING DOWN!!

INSIDE MOMMA BEAR'S IN-HOME BEAUTY SALON...

CHIEF YELLOWSHIRT *GONE?* YVONNE, THIS *HAIR-DO* IS ON THE HOUSE!

IN A HIGH-PRICED LIMO...

OH, MAH-MAH! HAS THE WORLD GONE MAD?

NONSENSE! YOUR FATHER'S IN LAS VEGAS AT A TRADE SHOW. HE'LL *NEVER* STEP DOWN.

DEEP INSIDE THE BINGO HALL...

SLOW DOWN, UNCLE CHESTER. MOVING TRUCK AT THE TRIBAL OFFICES. GOT IT.

SUPER INDIAN WILL BE THERE!

AT THE TRIBAL OFFICES, LENA MARIE SPORTS A STRANGE, GOTH LOOK...

REMOVE THE FURNITURE FROM THE CONFERENCE ROOM.

WE WILL SET UP THE INTERVIEWS HERE.

CARRIE, GET ME A LIST OF ALL THE *FULL BLOODS* FOR THE ON-CAMERA INTERVIEWS.

THAT'S PRIVILEGED INFO.

FORGET PROTOCOL. JUST DO IT.

CHIEF YELLOWSHIRT HAS TO AUTHORIZE THIS!

FOLKS, STAY BACK! MRS. LOGAN, WHAT'S GOING ON HERE?

CHIEF... BUT...THEY ARE? IT'S OKAY, THEN? REALLY.

DOWN WITH THE CHIEF!

GO DOWN TO I-T AND TELL AMBER TEETER IT'S NOT RIGHT UP HERE.

YOU GOT IT!

WHOOSHING THROUGH THE TRIBAL OFFICES...

I'D *FLY*. . . BUT THE CEILINGS ARE SO LOW IN HERE.

CHIEF YELLOWSHIRT'S ADMINISTRATION IS *STILL* INTACT.

MAY I OFFER YOU A FREE BINGO PACK AND COFFEE?

MY TREAT, Y'ALL!

LENA'S STRANGELY GENEROUS TODAY!

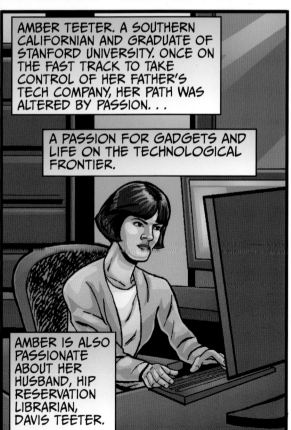

AMBER TEETER. A SOUTHERN CALIFORNIAN AND GRADUATE OF STANFORD UNIVERSITY. ONCE ON THE FAST TRACK TO TAKE CONTROL OF HER FATHER'S TECH COMPANY, HER PATH WAS ALTERED BY PASSION. . .

A PASSION FOR GADGETS AND LIFE ON THE TECHNOLOGICAL FRONTIER.

AMBER IS ALSO PASSIONATE ABOUT HER HUSBAND, HIP RESERVATION LIBRARIAN, DAVIS TEETER.

IF ONLY THAT ONE BIRD WOULD SMASH THAT STINKING BLOCK...

EXCUSE ME... MS. TEETER...

THERE IS SOMETHING *ODD* HAPPENING IN THE LOBBY!

BACK IN THE MOTOR HOME. . .

AT THE BINGO HALL, LENA MARIE BRIEFS HER NEW SECURITY DETAIL...

ONCE THE BLOOD MOBILE GETS HERE, Y'ALL WILL BE ON CROWD CONTROL.

EVERY ONE DONATES. GET ME?

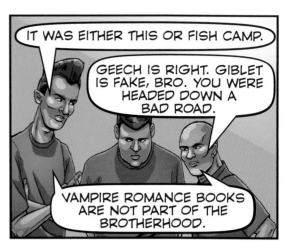

IT WAS EITHER THIS OR FISH CAMP.

GEECH IS RIGHT. GIBLET IS FAKE, BRO. YOU WERE HEADED DOWN A BAD ROAD.

VAMPIRE ROMANCE BOOKS ARE NOT PART OF THE BROTHERHOOD.

SOUP, WHAT'S WITH LENA'S "ROGUE"-LIKE WHITE STRIPED HAIR?

WE'RE ALL IN EXPENDABLE RED. YOU KNOW WHAT HAPPENS TO RED SHIRTS...

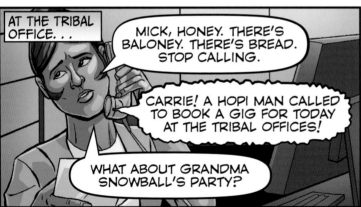

AT THE TRIBAL OFFICE...

MICK, HONEY. THERE'S BALONEY. THERE'S BREAD. STOP CALLING.

CARRIE! A HOPI MAN CALLED TO BOOK A GIG FOR TODAY AT THE TRIBAL OFFICES!

WHAT ABOUT GRANDMA SNOWBALL'S PARTY?

UH-OH...YOU'RE RIGHT. GRANDMA HAS A RIGHT TO THE BLUES. I'LL CALL THAT HOPI GUY BACK AND...

WAIT...THERE'S A HOPI GUY ON HIS WAY HERE FOR A BLOOD DRIVE. HONEY, CALL UNCLE CHESTER. SOMETHING'S UP.

WHOA...LAST TIME I DID THAT THERE WAS A RIOT. WE SHOULD GET OUR BOY HUBERT A CELL PHONE...

WOOF!

I'LL FIND SUPER INDIAN! PARTICLE THEORY CAN WAIT!

SAFE FROM DEADLY SUNLIGHT, BLUD KWAN'TUM SLEEPS WITHIN A HIDDEN COMPARTMENT INSIDE THE MOTOR HOME...

HE DRIFTS BETWEEN THE LIVING AND THE DEAD...

REMEMBERING. . .

MY ANCESTORS ARRIVED IN THE NEW WORLD WITH JUAN DE ONATE IN FIFTEEN EIGHTY-EIGHT.

THEY WERE BRAVE SPANISH NOBLES WHO CAME TO TAME THE SAVAGES. . .

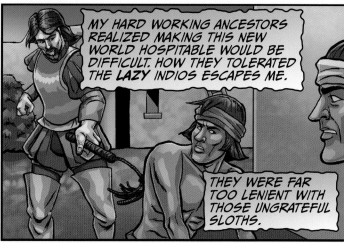

MY HARD WORKING ANCESTORS REALIZED MAKING THIS NEW WORLD HOSPITABLE WOULD BE DIFFICULT. HOW THEY TOLERATED THE **LAZY** INDIOS ESCAPES ME.

THEY WERE FAR TOO LENIENT WITH THOSE UNGRATEFUL SLOTHS.

THOSE SAVAGES CLUNG TO THEIR BACKWARDS SOCIETY.

THEY PLOTTED TO TAKE BACK THE LAND WE RIGHTLY CLAIMED FOR SPAIN.

MY GREAT-GREAT-GREAT GRANDFATHER INIGO MONTOYA GOMEZ CHAVEZ WOULD **NEVER** FORGET THEIR CRIMES.

HE VOWED REVENGE ON THOSE INDIGENOUS DEMONS!

THE INSOLENCE! THOSE RUTHLESS, BLOODTHIRSTY INDIOS BURNED THE CHURCH, KILLED THE PRIESTS AND ATTACKED MY FAMILY.

MANY YEARS LATER, MY FAMILY COULD HARDLY RECALL THOSE NATIVE HEATHENS AND THEIR BLOODY INSURRECTION.

AS THEY WATCHED "CHICO AND THE MAN," I SEETHED WITH RAGE.

EVEN WHILE STUDYING AT COLLEGE...

...THOSE INDIOS STOOD IN MY WAY!

BEGAY'S WORK ABOUT POPAY'S PUEBLO REVOLT IS MORE COMPELLING.

SORRY, CHAVEZ.

THEY INTERFERED WITH MY LOVE LIFE...

AI, PAPI! WE ALL HAVE SOME INDIO IN US – I'M PART OHKAY OWINGEH!

POPAY WAS FROM THERE!

HOW MY SPANISH BLOOD BOILED!

WHEN MY BELOVED ABUELITA HINTED SHE WAS PART INDIAN, IT WAS THE FINAL STRAW. I BECAME ESTRANGED FROM MY FAMILY.

I WOULD NOT STAY WITH THESE TRAITORS ANOTHER SECOND!

DESTITUTE, I FOUND A PLACE I COULD WORK OUT MY RAGE.

THE BUREAU OF INDIAN AFFAIRS.

WHEN MY SUPERIOR RETIRED, I EXPECTED TO TAKE HIS PLACE. WHAT DID THEY DO? THEY HIRED A HOPI!

I LOATHED MY WORK AS MUCH AS I LOATHED THE INDIANS I WAS HIRED TO SERVE.

PAPERWORK... DEADLINES... DISGRUNTLED INDIOS...

LOST MY FORMS AGAIN, YOU IDIOT!?

MRS. CHEE, GIVE ME ANOTHER CHANCE...

PAY ME WHAT I'M OWED, MONKEY BOY!

MY BOSS, THE HOPI *POKEMONEMPTEWA*, WAS UNAWARE OF MY DEEP-SEATED HOSTILITY.

WHAT OUR DEPARTMENT NEEDS IS AN ADVENTURE. I MET A GUY AT I-GAG WHO DOES TREKS TO MEXICO!

POKEMONEMPTEWA HIRED A BLOW-HARD LAKOTA TOUR GUIDE, BRODY BORDEAUX. HE MADE MANY PROMISES.

HOKA-HEY! EXCITEMENT AWAY!

TWO WEEKS AWAY FROM MY BUREAUCRATIC SINK-HOLE SOUNDED GOOD TO ME.

IN THE DARK REACHES OF THE TRIBAL OFFICES...

GOOD ONE! THOSE PIGS DON'T STAND A CHANCE!

HA HA! HA! HEE! HA! HEE! HAAA!

THAT'S SUPER INDIAN'S VOICE.

GAMING ON DUTY IS RARELY A SENSIBLE CHOICE!

HEY DIOGI! YOU'LL NEVER BELIEVE THE SKILLS MS. TEETER HAS WITH "ANGRY BIRDS!"

HOW CUTE! I THINK HE WANTS SOMETHING.

BARK! BARK! BARK! BARK!

THE TRIBAL ENROLLMENT FORMS ARE SAFE!

YET, YOUR ENEMIES DRAW NIGH!

HOW SIMPLE IT WOULD HAVE BEEN TO GIVE THE HOPI A SLIGHT PUSH OVER THE HIGH CLIFFS.

IF SOMETHING AWFUL HAPPENED TO HIM ON THE TREK, I WAS IN LINE TO TAKE HIS JOB.

ALAS, TOO MANY WITNESSES.

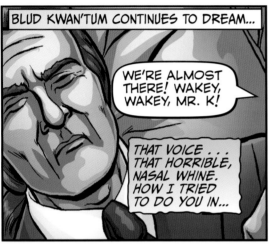

BLUD KWAN'TUM CONTINUES TO DREAM...

WE'RE ALMOST THERE! WAKEY, WAKEY, MR. K!

THAT VOICE . . . THAT HORRIBLE, NASAL WHINE. HOW I TRIED TO DO YOU IN...

WELCOME, B-I-A TEAM!

WE'LL BE ZIPLINING THROUGH ANCIENT RUINS, THEN TOURING A REAL BAT CAVE!

THE CHICOMOZTEC MAY HAVE FILLED ONE CAVE WITH GOLD!

CHAVEZ, NO!

SUICIDE? FOLLY?

NO!

RICHES AND GLORY WERE MINE!

AS I FLEW DOWN THE ZIPLINE, I SPOTTED A GLOW.

A *GOLDEN* GLOW.

HAH! STUPID INDIOS! THIS SON OF SPAIN HAS GOTTEN THE BEST OF YOU!

YOUR TREASURES ARE NOW *MINE!!!*

EARTHQUAKE? NO!!

RRRUMMMBLE

KRRUNCH!!

WH-WHO?

WHAT DO YOU WANT FROM ME?

YOU *STEAL* YOU *DIE!*

AT THE TRIBAL OFFICE...

YOU DO IT BECAUSE *MR. K* DEMANDS IT, Y'ALL. COWBOY UP AND GET THOSE *ELDERS* OVER HERE *PRONTO!*

HOW DID LENA GET ALL HAMMER HORRORED?

THIS DOESN'T LOOK GOOD, DIOGI!

WILL BLUD KWAN'TUM GET AWAY WITH THE GOLD? HOW HIGH WILL LENA'S HAIR GET? WILL GRANDMA SNOWBALL SING THE BLUES?

FIND OUT IN
"THE CURSE OF BLUD KWAN'TUM, PART II!"

SUSAN LA FLESCHE PICOTTE, MD.

The First Female Native American Doctor in the United States

Susan La Flesche was born on the Omaha Reservation in northeastern Nebraska in 1865. Her parents Chief Joseph La Flesche (Iron Eyes) and his wife, Mary (One Woman), educated their children in traditional ways, but also knew change was inevitable. Her father advocated education and building relationships with white reform groups. Susan's sister, Susette, had enrolled in the Elizabeth Institute for Young Ladies in New Jersey and became a national sensation after becoming an advocate for the Ponca Tribe, testifying at the famous trial of Luther Standing Bear. Susette aided in the return of the Ponca to their tribal lands, then paved the way for her siblings towards the dominant society. Susan also attended the Elizabeth Institute, returning home at age 17 to teach at the Quaker Mission School on the reservation.

Susan was always fascinated with traditional healers and medicine. As a girl, she watched a sick Indian woman die because the local white doctor would not give her care. "It was only an Indian and it did not matter. The doctor preferred hunting for prairie chickens rather than visiting poor, suffering humanity," she recalled. This incident and others influenced her to choose a medical career.

Susan nursed non-Native ethnologist Alice Fletcher back to health after a bout of inflammatory rheumatism, and she became Susan's champion. Susan finished her education at the Hampton Institute in Virginia. With the assistance of Martha Waldron and Alice Fletcher, Susan was the first person to receive federal aid to complete a three-year medical degree program at Woman's Medical College of Pennsylvania. In 1889, she graduated a year early and at the top of her class. Susan was the first American Indian woman in the United States to receive a medical degree.

She returned home to provide health care to the Omaha people. With her excellent command of English and the Omaha language, she served as a mediator between the Indians and the government, helping to resolve many disputes. In 1894, she married Henry Picotte and they raised two sons.

Susan's lifelong dream to establish a reservation hospital to care for her people became a reality in January 1913. Funded by a variety of sources, it was the first hospital built for an Indian reservation not funded by government money. Serving over 1,300 Indian and non-white patients, "Dr. Sue" cared for patients day and night.

An Indian advocate, health care reformer and tireless physician, she passed away in 1915 at age 50. Susan championed reform, but never abandoned her tribal roots. Susan's building is still in use today as the Dr. Susan La Flesche Picotte Memorial Hospital, and was declared a National Historic Landmark in 1992.

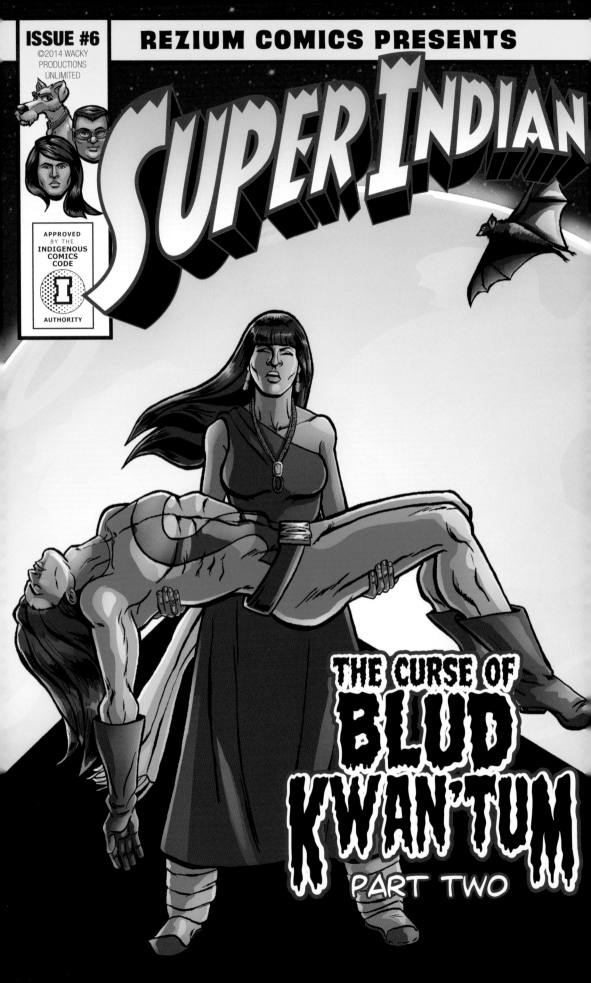

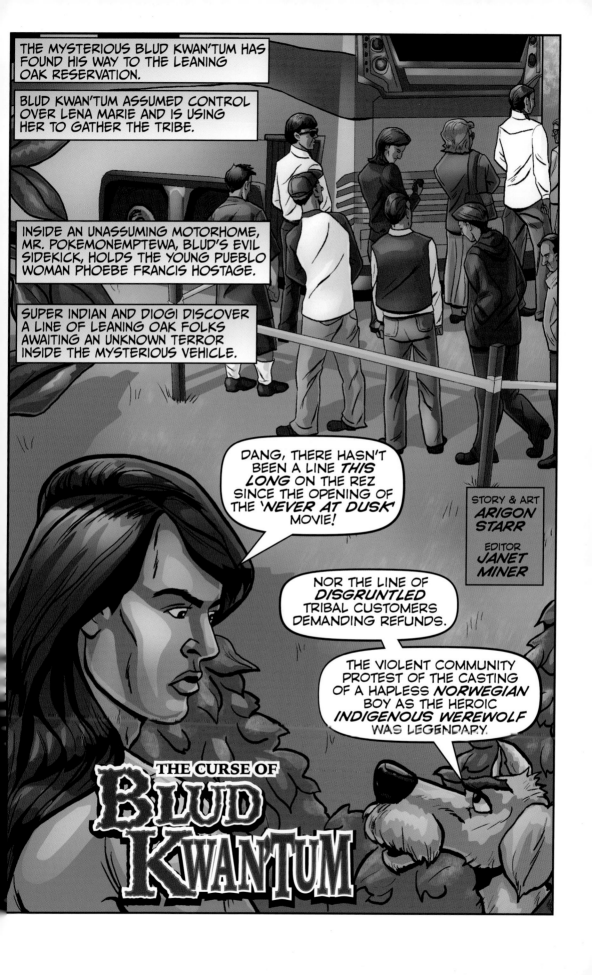

INSIDE THE MOTOR HOME, BLUD KWAN'TUM CONTINUES TO DREAM AND REMEMBER. . .

"THE LEGENDS WERE TRUE. THE AZTEC SHAMAN WAS REAL. BECAUSE I DARED TO POCKET THEIR GOLDEN TREASURE, I WAS SENTENCED TO DIE."

SCREEEEEECH!

AAA-III-EEEE!

SON OF SPAIN, FEEL THE *WRATH* OF. . .

THE BAT!

THE BAT REQUIRES A *BLOOD SACRIFICE.* DRAIN AS MANY INDIOS AS YOU CAN, FILL YOUR VEINS WITH THEIR LIFE FORCE.

FOR TO LIVE AGAIN, YOU MUST BECOME A *FULL-BLOOD* INDIO.

BECOME WHAT YOU *DESPISE,* SON OF SPAIN!

"THE BATS RETURNED ME TO BASE CAMP."

"I REGAINED CONSCIOUSNESS IN ALBUQUERQUE. THE FIRST FACE I SAW WAS MY HOPI BOSS.

HE LOOKS LIKE HE'S WAKING UP! CHAVEZ! YOU'RE *ALIVE!*

"POKEMONEMPTEWA WAS MY FIRST VICTIM."

"MY FORMER BOSS BECAME MY MAIN MINION. I ASSUMED CONTROL OF THE AGENCY."

"HE ALSO MADE SURE I HAD *PLENTY* OF *VICTIMS* AT *THE B-I-A*."

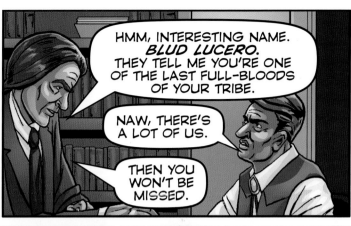

HMM, INTERESTING NAME. *BLUD LUCERO.* THEY TELL ME YOU'RE ONE OF THE LAST FULL-BLOODS OF YOUR TRIBE.

NAW, THERE'S A LOT OF US.

THEN YOU WON'T BE MISSED.

NOO-OOO!

AAAHH!

ONE INDIAN DOWN... THREE-HUNDRED AND SIXTY-FOUR TO GO! AN INDIAN A DAY KEEPS THE AZTEC CURSE AWAY!

"VICTIMS BECAME MY EMPLOYEES AT A BUSY CALL CENTER."

"WITH INDIAN BLOOD CAME NUMEROUS SMALL BUSINESS LOANS, TAX BENEFITS AND GOVERNMENT CONTRACTS."

"WE VISITED EVERY NATIVE TRADE SHOW AND CONFERENCE. SELECTING VICTIMS WAS KEY."

A CALL-IN CENTER! WE'VE BEEN WANTING TO DEVELOP ONE IN WAMPANOAG COUNTRY.

I'M *KELLY KWAN'TUM.* NICE TO MEET YOU! LET'S DISCUSS THIS OVER DINNER!

"ANOTHER *PERFECT* NAME."

"LENA MARIE SAID THE LEANING OAK RESERVATION HAS MORE FULL-BLOODS PER SQUARE INCH THAN ANYWHERE ELSE."

"I'LL BECOME A FULL-BLOOD INDIAN BY NIGHTFALL!"

"ONCE I'M A FULL-BLOOD, I WILL CONQUER ALL OF THE AMERICAS WITH MY SLAVE INDIOS."

"THEN, I WILL RETURN TO MEXICO WITH MY SLAVE ARMY TO CLAIM MY GOLDEN FORTUNE...AT LAST!"

AT THE ELDER'S CENTER. . .

GRANDMA SNOWBALL'S CAKE IS LIT AND THE FIRE ALARM HASN'T GONE OFF!

GIVE HER A ROUND OF APPLAUSE!

YOU PROMISED ME C-C-R, MICK LOGAN! "LODI" OR "PROUD MARY," STAT!

IT'S MY BIRTHDAY, SO NONE OF THAT OLD STUFF!

EDDIE VEDDER OR NOTHING!

GENERAL BEAR TAKES CHARGE. . .

THIS IS A TICKET HOLDERS LINE!

EVERYBODY'S GOT TO HAVE A TICKET.

YOU! YOU GOT A TICKET?

SURE, I HAVE A TICKET!

ALL RIGHT, GET BACK IN LINE!

POKEMONEMPTEWA PROMISED ENTERTAINMENT. WE PROMISED HIM ELDERS.

SOMEONE HAS FAILED ME.

WHERE ARE MICK AND THE BAND? THEY SHOULD ALREADY BE HERE!

WHO IS THIS GUY WITH A BLOOD DRIVE AND FILM CREW? TWO THINGS I NEVER WOULD HAVE PUT TOGETHER.

INSIDE BLUD'S LUXURY MOTORHOME. . .

MR. K, MY *INDIANOMETER* SAYS YOU ARE ONLY EIGHTY PERCENT INDIAN.

I *MUST* BECOME A FULL-BLOOD.

HUNDREDS WAIT OUTSIDE. THEY MAY NOT BE ENOUGH!

AFTER I ABSORB THE POPULATION HERE, TEST ME AGAIN. IF I'M NOT AT ONE HUNDRED PERCENT, I WILL DRAIN OUR CAPTIVE.

WHAT'S SO SPECIAL ABOUT *HER*?

SHE HAS A *DESTINY* TO FUFILL. I'VE SEEN IT! I WILL *STEAL* HER FUTURE AND HER *POWER!*

DON'T MOVE. DON'T EVEN *BREATHE!*

OUTSIDE, THE BAND ARRIVES...

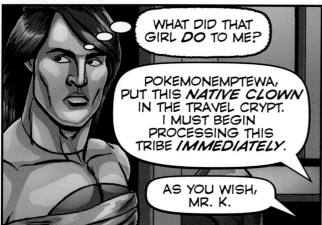

SO, WHEN GIBLET TELLS HER DAD THAT THERE'S SOMETHING "DIFFERENT" ABOUT CLIVE...

GENERAL, I WOULD NOT HAVE PEGGED YOU AS A *NEVER AT DUSK* FAN.

ZIP IT WHILE THEY PLAY "FRYBREAD BABY."

JUST BECAUSE YOU DON'T LIKE GIBLET AND CLIVE AS MUCH AS SELENE AND THOSE "UNDERWORLD" VAMPIRES...

DO *NOT* SPEAK HER NAME, *SPARKLY VAMPIRE LOVER!*

BARK BARK
BARK BARK BARK

AT THE SAME MOMENT, DIOGI DESPERATELY TRIES TO GET GENERAL BEAR'S ATTENTION. . .

BARK BARK
BARK
BARK
BARK

OH, THAT MY VOCAL PROWESS COULD OVERPOWER THE RAW OVER-AMPLIFICATION OF MICK LOGAN'S BLUES ENSEMBLE! I WILL BARK MYSELF INTO HOARSE SILENCE UNTIL I AM ACKNOWLEDGED!

BARK BARK BARK BARK BARK

INSIDE BLUD'S MOBILE HOME...

NO ONE WILL FIND YOU INSIDE MY CRYPT! I WILL *HONOR YOU* AS MY *FINAL VICTIM* AND MEMBER OF MY *ARMY OF INDIOS!*

YOU *WON'T* GET AWAY WITH THIS!

YOUR *CLOWN CRIES* ARE PATHETIC!

FOOM!

OH DANG. *NO* SUPER POWERS... *NO WAY OUT!*

KA'WAIKA WOMAN! FOLLOW ME TO SAFETY!

WHA-A-A? GOTTA GET UP... SOMEHOW...

THIS WAY!

WAIT! WAIT! I'M RIGHT BEHIND YOU...

YOWWWW!

CRASH!

WHERE THE HECK AM I? WHO AM I?

HERE'S OUR OTHER HIT, "GOT MY COBELL BLUES!"

MUST BE AN ALTERNATIVE UNIVERSE!

AND THEY TOLD ME GIBLET WAS JUST IN THE BOOKS!

YOU'RE... YOU'RE... REAL!

WHICH GIBLET ARE YOU? PINING GIBLET OR POWER GIBLET?

THESE PEOPLE LOOK FAMILIAR. BUT NOT! HEY, THAT GUY IN THE RED SHIRT LOOKS LIKE HE KNOWS WHAT'S GOING ON.

WHEN THE FINAL MOVIE COMES OUT, YOU'LL SEE LUKUS ISN'T THAT CREEPY! MYRA! COME BACK!

THANK GOODNESS SOMEONE KNOWS ME! GIBLET! *I AM GIBLET!*

REALLY? *REALLY?* WOW!

HEY...YOU'RE *MORE* THAN JUST A RED SHIRT!

I SEE HIS LIFE, WHO HE IS.. JUST BY *TOUCHING HIM.*

WHOA... RECONSIDER THE TIGHTS!

GENERAL BEAR... *KUNG FU FAN* AND PART-TIME *SUPER HERO SIDEKICK.*

DON'T SAY THAT TOO LOUD. NOBODY NEEDS TO KNOW.

THE KUNG FU OR SIDEKICK PART?

HIGHLY IRREGULAR. THAT WOMAN IS NOT A TRIBAL MEMBER NOR A RESERVATION RESIDENT....

YET....SHE *EXUDES* POWER...

WAIT...THOSE ARE ALL OF OUR TRADITIONAL FOLKS... HOW DID THEY FIND OUT? BETTER CALL AMBER TEETER...

ALWAYS... ELDERS FIRST!

NO NEED, MRS. LOGAN. SHE'S *TIED UP* AT THE MOMENT.

IN THE I-T DEPARTMENT... *NO ONE* CAN HEAR YOU *SCREAM.*

GET ME OUT OF HERE! THOSE PEOPLE... *THEY'RE EVIL!*

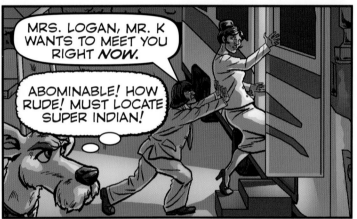

SUPER INDIAN USES WHAT'S LEFT OF HIS SUPER-CONCENTRATION TO TRANSMIT A SIGNAL TO DIOGI...

DIOGI! I'M IN BLUD'S MOBILE! THEY HAVE MY PARENTS! POWERS DRAINED... HELP ME!

URR?

URR?

GIVE THEM A LOLLIPOP AND SEND THEM TO THE BINGO HALL.

YES, MR. K!

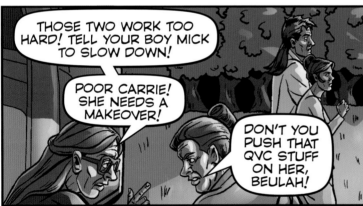

THOSE TWO WORK TOO HARD! TELL YOUR BOY MICK TO SLOW DOWN!

POOR CARRIE! SHE NEEDS A MAKEOVER!

DON'T YOU PUSH THAT QVC STUFF ON HER, BEULAH!

DEE-OH-GEE? DOESN'T THAT SPELL 'DOG?'

DANG! DIOGI! HE WAS RIGHT HERE... BARKING AT ME.

SOMETHING'S WRONG!

WOW! MY EARS ARE WONKY! I HEARD SOMEONE SAY THEY WERE TRAPPED AND NEEDED DAVINCI...OR LUIGI?

WEIRD! DAVINCI? THAT SOUNDS LIKE...DIOGI!

MEANWHILE, IN THE BINGO HALL...

NATIVE AMERICAN ZOMBIES.

SLAVES TO THE WILL OF BLUD KWAN'TUM!

GURRGGLE. GRAAK!

OUTSIDE THE BINGO HALL...

A ONCE VITAL COMMUNITY... REDUCED TO A GHOST TOWN!

HOWEVER....THERE ARE STILL SIGNS OF LIFE!

GIBLET, STAY BEHIND ME.

DON'T TELL *ANYBODY* ABOUT THIS CLOSET.

OR THAT YOUR SIDEKICK OUTFIT'S IN HERE AND THAT *HUBERT'S* REALLY *SUPER INDIAN?*

YOU AND YOUR VAMPIRE POWERS ARE CREEPING ME OUT!

MAYBE CLIVE HASN'T TURNED YOU YET. GIBLET DOESN'T HAVE MIND-READING POWER IN THE BOOK.

MY TEETH AREN'T POINTY! I LACK BLOOD LUST. ARE MY EYES RUSTY RED?

MR. K, THAT'S THE LAST OF THEM. THIS MANGY ANIMAL WAS OUTSIDE THE VEHICLE. ARE YOU HUNGRY FOR DOG?

MMM... PUPPY STEW.

CHECK MY BLOOD QUANTUM. I MUST BE CLOSE TO *ONE HUNDRED PERCENT* NOW!

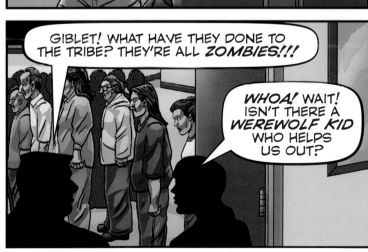

GIBLET! WHAT HAVE THEY DONE TO THE TRIBE? THEY'RE ALL *ZOMBIES!!!*

WHOA! WAIT! ISN'T THERE A *WEREWOLF KID* WHO HELPS US OUT?

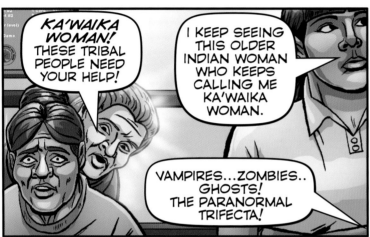

I AM. . . **KA'WÄIKA WOMAN!**

WHOA! I THOUGHT SUPER INDIAN WAS COOL...BUT DANG!

I GOTTA KNOW... DO YOU HAVE SUPER POWERS?

YES, I AM *POWERFUL.* YET, THERE ARE MANY IN *DANGER!* WE MUST *SAVE* THEM! BY MY SIDE, MEGA BEAR!

SEE AS I SEE, MEGA BEAR.

JUST BY TOUCHING ME?

BLUD KWAN'TUM IS A VAMPIRE WHO WANTS TO BECOME A FULL BLOOD INDIAN. MOVIE AND BLOOD MOBILE ARE LURES TO BITE INDIANS. ALL RIGHTY!

AND...WE ARE FLYING. OH MY!

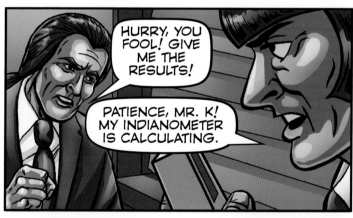

HURRY, YOU FOOL! GIVE ME THE RESULTS!

PATIENCE, MR. K! MY INDIANOMETER IS CALCULATING.

NINETY-FIVE PERCENT. YOU ARE MORE INDIAN THAN I AM.

NOT GOOD ENOUGH! HAVE I BITTEN EVERYONE? WAIT - THAT BOY IN THE CLOWN SUIT! BRING HIM TO ME!

THE LAST PLACE I SAW PEOPLE WAS IN LINE AT THE BLOODMOBILE. SERIOUSLY...WHO FILMS PEOPLE THEN TAKES THEIR BLOOD?

LO! A CANINE APPROACHES!

BARK! BARK! BARK! YAP!

EASY, BOY! THIS IS...

DIOGI. THE THIRD OF LEANING OAK'S SUPER HERO TRIUMVIRATE.

THE TAINTED CHEESE GAVE YOU SUPER POWERS, TOO. INTELLIGENT, LITERATE, WITH THE POWER OF SPEECH.

REFRESHING! ANOTHER HERO I MIGHT CONFIDE IN! KA'WAIKA WOMAN, YOU MAY BE OUR ONLY HOPE.

I FEAR SUPER INDIAN IS *LOST*...ANOTHER HELPLESS VICTIM OF BLUD KWAN'TUM!

WAIT...I HEARD DIOGI *TALK*! HUBERT? IN *DANGER*? NO!

THEY...MADE... ME *MAD!*

HOLD ON, *SUPER INDIAN!!*

LENA, *MOVE!* I DON'T WANT TO HURT YOU!

LITTLE MAN! YOU ARE NO MATCH FOR MY MASTER!

MEGA BEAR! DIOGI FOUND HIM!

THERE'S SOMEONE UNUSUAL OUT THERE...I CAN FEEL IT. NO POWERS...STILL DEFENSELESS...

OUTSIDE OF THE MOTOR HOME...

BEHOLD, I AM THE *LIBERATOR* OF YOU SAD, WORTHLESS NATIVE AMERICANS.

I AM *MORE INDIO* THAN YOU'LL *EVER* BE!

MEET YOUR LORD AND RULER...

BLUD KWANTUM!

MR. K...YOU NEED TO BITE ONE OF THESE *COSTUMED CLOWNS* TO BECOME A *FULL-BLOOD!*

BRING ME THE *BIG* ONE!

DON'T FEAR, MY SUPER INDIAN! KA'WAIKA WOMAN IS HERE!

WHO? WHAT?

TAINTED CHEESE...REZIUM... POWERS IN DEVELOPMENT....

KA'WAIKA... LAGUNA... TRAVEL AGENCY... I-GAG... LENA...

ENERGY EXCHANGE... THE CATALYST!

THE FORCE THROWS THEM FROM THE MOTOR HOME.

ON THE FAR SIDE OF THE MOTOR HOME...

KA'WAIKA WOMAN, ARE YOU OKAY?

DAZED...SUPER INDIAN, WHAT HAPPENED?

KA'WAIKA WOMAN LIKES WHAT SHE *SEES!*

DANG...IT'S *BACK!* MY *POWERS* ARE BACK!

HEH, HEH, HEH. YOU'RE TOO LATE *CLOWN MAN!* I'VE *DRAINED HIM!*

MEGA BEAR! NO!!

FINE. YOU WANT TO *BITE* PEOPLE? YOU SHOULD HAVE *BITTEN ME.*

YOU WANT SOME OF *THIS?* COME AND GET YOU *SOME* OF *THIS!*

NDN

SUPER INDIAN! NO! YOUR POWERS COULD *TRANSFER* TO HIM! STOP!!

YOU SHOULD HAVE STAYED IN CLOWN COLLEGE, INDIO! PREPARE TO *DIE!*

AS BLUD'S RAZOR SHARP FANGS SINK INTO SUPER INDIAN'S FLESH, DARKNESS DESCENDS.

CHOMP!

NO! SUPER INDIAN MUST *LIVE!*

HE MUSN'T BECOME ONE OF BLUD'S *ZOMBIES!*

GUGGHH... ACKKK... GRRGHH...

I'VE *DONE* IT! I AM A *FULL-BLOOD!*

SO MUCH FOR A RIDICULOUS *AZTEC CURSE!* HA! HA! HA!

I AM *KA'WAIKA WOMAN!* THE POWER OF THE ANCESTORS RESIDES WITHIN ME!

PHOEBE FRANCIS, YOUR ANCESTORS' POWERS ARE NO MATCH FOR MINE. TOO *LITTLE,* TOO *LATE!*

DON'T TOUCH THE SUIT!

SON OF SPAIN... ALBUQUERQUE...THE B-I-A...MOUNTAINS OF MEXICO...THE *GOLD!*

RICHES YOU'LL *NEVER* HAVE, WRETCHED INDIO WITCH! MY ZOMBIE ARMY WILL RISE!

THE *BATS*...HUNGRY... SO VERY...*HUNGRY*...

WHAT'S HAPPENING? THAT *SOUND*...

AFTER BLUD WAS DEFEATED, THE ZOMBIE CURSE WAS BROKEN.

DIOGI FIGURES PHOEBE'S POWERS WERE ACTIVATED BY A *SUB-ATOMIC CATALYST* IN MY REZIUM-TAINTED BLOOD.

I'M GRATEFUL TO BE A MEMBER OF *TEAM SUPER INDIAN*. I CAN FINALLY MAKE ALL THE GADGETS I'VE BEEN DREAMING OF!

I THINK YOU MIGHT HAVE A *FORCE* THAT COULD AWAKEN *POWERS* IN OTHER NATIVE PEOPLE.

KNOWING WHAT I KNOW NOW ANSWERS SO MANY NAGGING QUESTIONS. YOUR SECRET IS SAFE WITH ME, DUDE!

I'M GOING BACK TO MY TRIBE IN NEW MEXICO. MEGA BEAR...I'M SORRY I'M NOT REALLY '*GIBLET,*' THOUGH. YOU AND I CAN STILL BE LONG-DISTANCE '*DUSKERS!*'

I'M EVEN GOING BACK TO MY OLD JOB!

BEING AN ECO-TOUR DIRECTOR IS A GOOD COVER FOR KEEPING AN EYE ON OUR SACRED OBJECTS AND PLACES.

SON, I AM SO *PROUD* OF YOU! THAT TOOK GUTS TO LET THAT OLD SPAINARD BITE YOU!

AND NOW WE HAVE A SUPER HEROINE ON OUR TEAM! KA'WAIKA WOMAN IS *FIERCE!*

REAL SUPER INDIANS

MOSES YELLOWHORSE

First Full Blood Indian Pitcher in the Major Leagues

"Put in YellowHorse!" rose the chant from the throngs of Pittsburgh Pirates' fans at Forbes Field. The 5'10", 180 pound Pawnee from Oklahoma took the mound and fired his trademark smoking fastball.

Moses J. YellowHorse, or Mose as most knew him, was born on the Pawnee Reservation in 1898. Raised by his father Thomas and adopted mother Clara, Mose grew up on a large ranch, surrounded by tribal life. To Mose, the Pawnee Nation was everything. He eagerly learned and participated in his traditional ways. To help his family's finances, he performed with Pawnee Bill's Wild West Show and used rocks to capture small game.

Education was also important to the tribe. Mose attended the local Pawnee Agency School and completed his studies at Chilocco Indian School. Mose's friendliness, good humor and strong physique helped him find success on the school's base-ball team. In his first year, he was a winner with a perfect season (17-0) record.

In 1920, Mose played semi-pro ball with the Arkansas Travelers and went 21-7, leading the team to their first league championship. His success caught the attention of Barney Dreyfuss, the owner of the Pittsburgh Pirates. Dreyfuss brought YellowHorse to the big leagues at the tender age of 22. He was the first full-blood Indian to pitch in the major leagues.

Mose's easygoing personality and humor took Pittsburgh by surprise and endeared him to the fans, community and his teammates. In the two years he played with the Pirates, Mose pitched in 38 games with a record of 8 wins and 4 losses, with an earned run average of 3.93. Some of Mose's most memorable moments occurred during exhibition games in 1922. After being taunted and verbally abused by the notorious Ty Cobb, YellowHorse injured him so severely with a fastball that he had to be carried off the field. At another game in Oklahoma, YellowHorse struck out the mighty Babe Ruth.

Unfortunately, injuries and alcohol abuse cut short Mose's career. He played in the minor leagues until 1926. He returned to Pawnee and held a variety of odd jobs, but kept drinking. During this period, he was immortalized in the "Dick Tracy" comic book strip as "Chief YellowPony." "Dick Tracy" creator Chester Gould was also born near Pawnee and knew of YellowHorse and his accomplishments.

In 1945, Mose suddenly quit drinking and returned to baseball – as a ground-skeeper for the Ponca City ballclub, and to coach a team of all-Pawnee youth. He also became an honored elder in the community. YellowHorse passed away in 1964, but his memory lives on within the Pawnee Nation. Although Yel-lowHorse isn't a Baseball Hall of Fame inductee, his glove is enshrined and on display in the hallowed halls of Cooperstown.

HE SAVED A STRANDED HIKER *THEN* RAISED MONEY FOR THE AT-RISK YOUTH BASEBALL TEAM. MAVIS, I'VE *FALLEN HARD* FOR SUPER INDIAN.

SHE *FELL* FOR AN AT-RISK YOUTH?

NAW, FOR THAT *SUPER GUY,* WHAT'S HIS NAME?

COMMODORE COMMOD?

SUPER INDIAN! YEAH, THAT GUY.

I RESISTED HIS CHARMS, BUT NOW...I'M *TEAM SUPER INDIAN.*

SHE'S OUT OF HIS LEAGUE.

DEFINITELY *DOUBLE A.* NOT READY FOR *THE SHOW.*

AT GRANDMA LOGAN'S, LADEN WITH HER BINGO LOOT...

MY AUNT CECELIA WANTED THIS TOASTER.

TOASTALL

COOKER

A LOT OF PEOPLE ARE *HATING ON* MY GRANDMA.

BOYS, BRING IT ALL IN. GOTTA RUN! I'M LATE FOR THE GAME!

GRANDMA, WE HAD A DATE IN THE *REZIUM FORBIDDEN ZONE* TODAY!

SORRY, GRANDBABY. DUTY CALLS!

I THINK GRANDMA HAS A *GAMBLING* PROBLEM.

IN THE DARK OF NIGHT, A MYSTERIOUS PRESENCE LURKS OUTSIDE OF FLORA LOGAN'S HOME.

Your kitten will return when you start winning!

THE NEXT DAY. . .

GRANDMA, THERE'S AN 800-NUMBER TO CALL.

I KNOW. STOP WORRYING.

ARE YOU STILL MAD ABOUT BOB BARKER AND THE "PRICE IS RIGHT?"

IN ANOTHER PART OF THE BINGO HALL. . .

AND DON'T FORGET TO TELL HER I'LL BE *WATCHING*.

YOU GOT IT.

AFTER THE DROP. . .

TILLIE! WAIT! *WHO* GAVE YOU THAT BAG FOR GRANDMA? DON'T ENABLE HER!

SO *BUSY* TODAY, HUBERT.

LENA WANTS A BUDGET, PLANNING "REZCON TWO" AND GOTTA DELETE MY MYSPACE PAGE. LATER!

DON'T FOLLOW ME. YOU DON'T HAVE CLEARANCE TO BE IN THIS AREA!

GAH! SHE IS *SO MEAN!*

WHAT DID I *DO* TO HER? ALL SHE SEES IS *HIM*. STUPID SUPER INDIAN. I'LL ALWAYS BE IN HIS *SHADOW*.

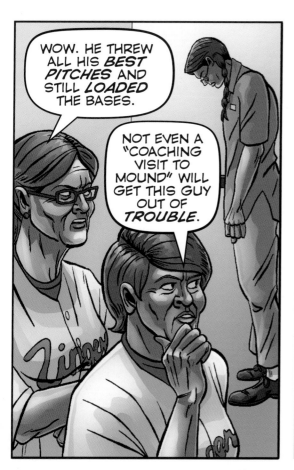

WOW. HE THREW ALL HIS *BEST PITCHES* AND STILL *LOADED* THE BASES.

NOT EVEN A "COACHING VISIT TO MOUND" WILL GET THIS GUY OUT OF *TROUBLE*.

GENERAL BEAR, POWER UP. WE NEED TO *SAVE* GRANDMA FROM HERSELF.

DONE.

MEET YOU AT GRANDMA'S HOUSE FOR SURVEILLANCE DUTY.

LATER, OUTSIDE OF GRANDMA LOGAN'S HOUSE. . .

WE'VE BEEN HERE FOR HOURS. I'M GETTING HUNGRY.

FIVE MORE MINUTES AND WE'LL GO GET A BURGER.

BARK!

MIGHT BE NAVAJO!

SKINWALKERS! DUDE! THIS IS SERIOUS!

LA-DAH-DAH-DEE-DEE-DUH... BEEE-GEEEN!

BEE-GEEN? WHAT IS THAT? SHINOB??

THE END.

About The Author

Arigon Starr is an enrolled member of the Kickapoo Tribe of Oklahoma. She grew up on the road as part of a military family. Her parents, Ken Wahpecome (Kickapoo) and mother Ruth (an enrolled Muscogee Creek) supported her artistic expressions, encouraging her to learn as much as possible about music, composition, art, and drama. Starr relocated to Los Angeles, where she worked behind the scenes at entertainment companies like Viacom Productions and Showtime Networks. In 1996, she left her corporate job behind and became a full-time musician.

Starr's first CD, *Meet the Diva*, was named Best Independent Recording at the Second Annual Native American Music Awards. Her second release, *Wind-Up*, contained the hit "Junior Frybread," which was named Song/Single of the Year at the Fourth Annual Native American Music Awards. In 2002, Wacky Productions released her third CD, *Backflip*, which featured Grammy-nominated country act BR549. Starr's fourth CD, *The Red Road – Original Cast Recording* was named the Best Contemporary CD at the 15th Annual First Americans in the Arts Awards and features a Who's Who of musical guest stars from Los Angeles and Nashville. Additionally, Arigon was named "Songwriter of the Year" by the Native American Music Awards and received a nomination for "Best Country CD" from Canada's Aboriginal Peoples Choice Awards.

Starr's music has taken her around the world including stops in London and the famous West Yorkshire Playhouse in Leeds, in addition to appearances at the New Orleans Jazz & Heritage Festival and at venues like Sky City and Isleta Casinos in New Mexico, the Gilcrease Museum in Tulsa and the National Museum of the American Indian in Washington, DC and New York City.

Starr has also gained fame for her acting and has been awarded two First Americans in the Arts Awards, the Maverick Award from the Los Angeles Women's Theater Project, and a Wordcraft Circle of Native Writers Award. Arigon is the playwright, composer and performer of *The Red Road*, a wild, wacky musical comedy from Native Voices at the Autry. The play garnered rave reviews from the Los Angeles Times and Daily Variety and has toured across the U.S. and Australia. Arigon also wrote and performed two original plays in *Red Ink*, a compilation of contemporary Native stories produced by the Mixed Blood Theater in Minneapolis. Additionally, Starr has appeared on television in Showtime's comedy, *Barbershop: The Series* and ABC's *General Hospital*.

Native Voices at the Autry and the Native Radio Theater project teamed with Starr for *Super Indian*, a radio comedy series she created which was taped before a live audience and broadcast in 2007. In July 2009, Starr taped a live radio version of her one-woman show *The Red Road*, directed by award-winning director/producer Dirk Maggs.

Her illustrations are in demand by high-profile clients such as the Autry National Center in Los Angeles, Healthy Aboriginal Network in Canada and the rock band Queen. In April 2011, Starr began publishing *Super Indian* online as a webcomic. The comic has boasted a new panel every Monday continuously for almost five years. *Super Indian Volume One* was published in 2012 to immediate acclaim and has been added to the curricula of multiple colleges and universities across the United States and Canada. Her work has been highlighted in the publications *First American Art* and *Native Peoples*. *Super Indian* will also be part of a special exhibition at the Heard Museum in Phoenix, Arizona in 2015 that features Native American super heroes.

She is also one of the founders of the Indigenous Narratives Collective (INC), a group of Native American comic book writers and artists. INC has released a group project (*INC's Universe #0*) and has released Starr's *Annumpa Luma: Code Talker*, the story of the first Choctaw Code Talkers as a mini-comic. The 12-page comic is part of a larger work, *Tales of the Mighty Code Talkers* that will be published by INC Comics.

Starr continues to write, act and perform and is represented by Kristene Wallis at the Wallis Agency. Starr is a member of the SAG-AFTRA, Actors Equity and the National Academy of Recording Arts and Sciences. She is based in Los Angeles.

Online at www.superindiancomics.com and www.arigonstarr.com.